W9-CYB-304

RIGHT ON, SISTER!

BY MORT GERBERG

GROSSETT & DUNLAP
A NATIONAL GENERAL CO.

Publishers   *New York*

For Lillian Flance Gerberg, who was my source . . .
and for Judith Mary Levine Gerberg, who made
this all happen.

Mort Gerberg is the author of
Boys Love Girls . . . More or Less
and, with Marcia Seligson and Avery Corman,
Whatever Happened To . . . ?
You Have A Hang-up If . . .
The Everything In The World That's
The Same As Something Else Book

COPYRIGHT © 1971 BY MORT GERBERG
ALL RIGHTS RESERVED
PUBLISHED SIMULTANEOUSLY IN CANADA

LIBRARY OF CONGRESS CATALOG CARD NUMBER: 70-144069
ISBN: 0-448-02215-x

PRINTED IN THE UNITED STATES OF AMERICA

1

"*Look at it this way, honey — freedom isn't everything.*"

"I'll tell you one thing — this is a helluva place
for meeting men."

"*My name is Judith Mary*
Berens-Levine-Press-Flancenbaum. Right on!"

"I just _can't_, honey — you _know_ that Saturday
is my day of protest."

"*I'll tell you one thing — since I joined the
Women's Liberation, I'm not as hung up
on myself as I used to be.*"

"She's one of the leaders of the Women's Liberation movement — the little bitch."

"Funny, he doesn't <u>look</u> like a male chauvinist pig."

"I'm sorry, but I didn't catch your names."

"What do you suggest that might persuade a beautiful and otherwise charming young creature to refrain from shooting her mouth off about Women's Lib?"

"A woman's work is never done."

"I suppose you could say that I'm _nouveau liberated_."

WINSOME
WINNIE WINGLE

Winsome Winnie Wingle
    strolls around town
Upstairs and downstairs
    in a sexy gown.
Doesn't feel exploited;
    she disregards the smirk,
"I'm better off than most,"
    she says,
      "Hooking's
      <u>honest</u> work."

FEMINIST MARY

Feminist Mary, quite contrary,
How does your movement grow?
Through radical stands and sharp demands
Attacking the status quo.

"*No . . . please, honey — not tonight . . . I've got to get up early tomorrow and march against male oppression.*"

"*Yessir — it looks like a long winter ahead.*"

"*Face it, Freddie — it's not just the egg roll;
it's our entire way of life.*"

"*Oh, we're very pleased — especially when you
consider that Sheila is the most
radical activist in the whole Women's Liberation.*"

*"Now that we've developed the power of speech,
keep your mouth shut!"*

"*He hates me . . . he hates Women's Liberation . . .
he hates me . . . he hates Women's Liberation. . . .*"

"*Since she started questioning our basic sex roles,
we're no longer living happily ever after.*"

"*I'm sorry, but I have to go now — it's time for my consciousness-raising group.*"

"And you call yourself an Equal Opportunity Employer?"

"It's basically the same old act, only with a little topical pizzazz added."

"My husband thinks I'm out demonstrating for equal rights for women."

"*Call me sentimental, darling, but first we'll
have to get the blessings
of my consciousness-raising group.*"

THINK
UPPITY

ROCK-A-BYE, BABY

Rock-A-Bye, Baby, you're on your own,
Mother must work and leave you alone.
When she goes out, she knows what to do,
She has a day-care center for you.

JACK, BE LIBERAL

Jack, be liberal, Jack be big;
Jack, don't be a chauvinist pig!

RIDE WITH A FROWN

Ride with a frown to a damp Jersey town
To see Miss America twirl in her crown;
Enacting her sex role with rings in her nose,
She'll be exploited wherever she goes.

MARY HAS A
PERSIAN LAMB

Mary has a Persian Lamb,
Its cost is much too high;
Poor Mary rearranged her life
To wed some wealthy guy.

"Congratulations! It's a sister!"

"It may not _look_ as sexy,
but it's a lot more gratifying."

"That doesn't apply to *me*. I don't *need* to be liberated.
I *am* liberated. I've *been* successful on my own—
and I could go back to work today if I wanted to—
with no hang ups—because I know my husband would let me!"

"*I just can't tolerate her 'more liberated
than thou' attitude.*"

"Hey, Dad, look! Mom's on the news!"

"My Marcia has always been so talented in so many
areas. I only hope she finds
a direction for herself and gets married."

"Well, I personally never did believe much — three clubs — in the vaginal orgasm."

"*My girl is very hot on Women's Lib. Do you have anything that can say 'I love you' without starting an argument?*"

"*Eight o'clock, Mrs. Lincoln — time to get up and start freeing the slaves.*"

*"Where do you stand on the question of
free day-care centers?"*

"*Better stay where you are, kiddo — everything makes
even less sense out here.*"

"*There may be merit to Women's Liberation, Edith,
but I'm not sure this is the best way to convince me.*"

"They give you a bop on the head, a roll in the hay, and right away they've invented a patriarchal society."

TO MARKET, TO CLEANERS

To market, to cleaners, to laundryroom sinks,
Home again, brood again, this system stinks!

A DILLER, A DOLLAR

A diller, a dollar, a Phi Beta scholar,
The boss can call you "Honey,"
But as long as you're doing equal work,
You should get equal money.

PRETTY MISS MUFFET

Pretty Miss Muffet sat on a tuffet
Auditioning for a new play.
A raunchy old backer began to attack her,
But a karate chop scared him away.

PETER, PETER,
PUMPKIN GROWER

Peter, Peter, pumpkin grower,
Had a wife, but didn't know her,
Until she screamed out from her shell
And then he got to know her well.

"*Mirror, mirror on the wall, who's the most
militant of them all?*"

"I *hate* it when they stare at us."

"*Poor Ralph. Apparently he's having a lot of
trouble making his alimony payments.*"

"Where the hell do you think you are, Henderson!"

"*Do you have anything that deals with them on an intellectual level?*"

"Would either of you girls like to comment on that viewpoint?"

"*Well, of course I'm in favor of being liberated.
It's just that I'm a bit concerned about
what happens to my charge account at Bonwit's.*"

"*Goddammit, Harry, I told you never to call me here!*"

"Well, at least it's becoming a more _honest_ contest."

*"And see, when you pick her up she cries,
'Right on, sister!'"*

"On the other hand, in every other kind of work,
you have the problem of being passed over for promotions,
raises, and never getting a fair chance for advancement . . ."

"You seem to have an ambivalent attitude toward your sexual identity."

"My dear Miss Gibson, if, all of a sudden, our great American success formula of using female breasts in ads makes me a male chauvinist pig, well then —oink! oink! oink!

YOUNG MS. HUBBARD

Young Ms. Hubbard went to the cupboard
To get herself a nice chop.
But the cupboard was bare, and that wasn't fair,
Her husband had said he would shop.

THERE WAS A SISTER, SHIRL

There was a sister, Shirl, whose
    upper lip did curl;
To fight the male supremists was her niche.
When she was tough she was very, very tough,
But when at her best she was a BITCH.

THERE WAS AN OLD WOMAN

There was an old woman who lived in a shoe,
She had so many children
She finally went out and campaigned
    to abolish abortion laws.

"*Please*, coach! Can't we *skip* the
old pat of encouragement!"

"Open wide and say 'Right on'."

"*I may not look it, Miss Daley, but I'm probably more empathetic to your cause than any other stud in the room.*"

"*Now <u>there's</u> an encouraging sign.*"

"Where do _you_ come off having a headache? In this house _I'm_ the one who's entitled to headaches."

"*You know what your problem is? I'll <u>tell</u> you what your problem is. Your problem is <u>ovary envy!</u>*"

"*Lay off love for a while. Your Venus is in
conjunction with Radical Feminists.*"

"*Of course, exploitation exists only in the minds
of the exploited . . .*"

"That's it? That's the extent of your whole argument?"

"I wouldn't mind becoming active in the movement; who knows, maybe someday I might even meet Miss Right-On."

"I think Helen and I have finally had it. This morning she put in a request for severance pay."

"Well, at least you still know who's boss,
don't you, old girl?"

"*Go ahead, Leonard . . . say something . . . I <u>dare</u> you!*"

*"We're collecting for Amy.
She's <u>not</u> going to have a baby."*

JACQUELINE HORNER

Jacqueline Horner
    stood on a corner
Watching the Libs march by.
After they'd gone she shouted,
    "Right on!"
And thought,
    "What a hep girl am I."

PUSSYCAT, PUSSYCAT

Pussycat, Pussycat, where did you go?
To see the lib ladies on the TV talk show.
Pussycat, Pussycat, what did you there?
I hit David Susskind in the head with a chair.

AS I WAS GOING TO ST. IVES

As I was going to St. Ives,
I met a man with seven wives —
    the male chauvinist pig!

SING A SONG OF PROTEST

Sing a song of protest, a war for women's rights,
Forty-million feminists getting into fights.
When the fights are over we'll all begin to groove,
Isn't that a crazy way for living to improve?

"O.K., O.K., but every night?"

"You will meet a beautiful, dark-haired girl from Women's Liberation who will tell you to go to hell."

"*You never heard of a lady guru? That just goes to show how unenlightened you are.*"

"*You and Dr. Whitehead also share a common ideology
— you're both male chauvinist pigs.*"

"*The congregation wants you to know we think you have a very nice speaking voice . . . and a good head on your shoulders . . . and you're very inspiring . . . but when you get right down to it, we don't like rabbis without beards.*"

*"Equal job opportunity connected to free day-care
centers; free day-care centers connected
to abortion laws; abortion laws connected to . . ."*

"*Your grievances are quite valid, Madam, but Bloomingdale's cannot be responsible for male chauvinism.*"

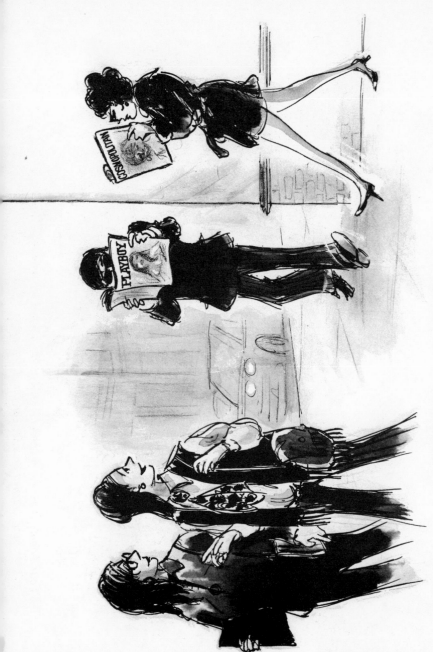

"Hold it, Ann — this I gotta see."

"Your honor, it is my contention that this whole trial would be much much _fairer_ if the learned counsel for the defense were wearing a bra!"

"*Why can't you just nag me the way you used to!*"

"*Listen, unless we get that equal-pay-for-equal-work thing settled, I don't <u>want</u> her to grow up to be president.*"